W9-BPM-683

NUMBER® CORNER

SECOND EDITION
STUDENT BOOK

GRADE
3

Published by The MATH LEARNING CENTER *Salem, Oregon*

Number Corner Second Edition Grade 3 Student Book

The Number Corner Grade 3 package consists of:

Number Corner Grade 3 Teachers Guide Volumes 1–3

Number Corner Grade 3 Teacher Masters

Number Corner Grade 3 Student Book

Number Corner Grade 3 Teacher Masters Answer Key

Number Corner Grade 3 Student Book Answer Key

Number Corner Grade 3 Components & Manipulatives

Assessment Guide:

• Number Corner Assessments

• Comprehensive Growth Assessment

Digital resources noted in italics.

The Math Learning Center, PO Box 12929, Salem, Oregon 97309. Tel 1 (800) 575-8130
www.mathlearningcenter.org

Prepared for publication using Mac OS X and Adobe Creative Suite.
Printed in the United States of America.

To reorder this book, refer to number 2NC3SB5 (package of 5).

QBN3901

06012020_LSC

Updated 2015-01-09.

Bridges in Mathematics is a standards-based K–5 curriculum that provides a unique blend of concept development and skills practice in the context of problem solving. It incorporates Number Corner, a collection of daily skill-building activities for students.

The Math Learning Center is a nonprofit organization serving the education community. Our mission is to inspire and enable individuals to discover and develop their mathematical confidence and ability. We offer innovative and standards-based professional development, curriculum, materials, and resources to support learning and teaching. To find out more, visit us at www.mathlearningcenter.org.

ISBN 978-1-60262-448-1

Number Corner Grade 3
Student Book

Problem String Work Space begins on page A1 at the back of the Number Corner Student Book.

© The Math Learning Center | mathlearningcenter.org

March

April

May

🗓️ Multiplication Models page 1 of 2

1 Draw a line from each of the multiplication models to the matching equation. Then fill in the blank to show the answer.

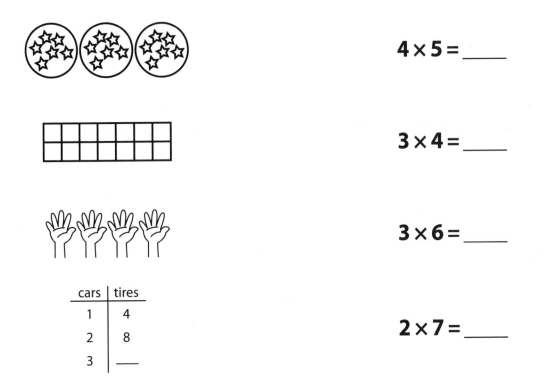

$4 \times 5 =$ _____

$3 \times 4 =$ _____

$3 \times 6 =$ _____

$2 \times 7 =$ _____

2 Make a sketch of one of the multiplication models you studied this month to match each expression. Choose a different model for each expression.

2×4	
3×5	
6×2	

NAME _____ |**DATE** _____

Multiplication Models page 2 of 2

3 One day, Jacob saw 4 ladybugs sitting on a leaf. Each ladybug had 4 spots.

 a How many spots in all? Use numbers, labeled sketches, or words to help solve this problem.

 b Which equation matches this problem? Fill in the bubble to show.

 ○ $4 + 4 = 8$ spots   ○ $4 \times 4 = 16$ spots

 ○ $4 + 4 + 4 = 12$ spots   ○ $4 - 4 = 0$ spots

4 Write a story problem to match this equation: $8 \times 2 = 16$.

5 **CHALLENGE** There was a tree with 3 branches. On each branch there were 3 cages. In each cage there were 3 birds. How many birds in all? Use numbers, labeled sketches, or words to help solve this problem. Show all your work.

2

NAME _____ | DATE _____

Loops & Groups Record Sheet

	Teacher	Students
1st Turn		
2nd Turn		
3rd Turn		
4th Turn		
Sum		

NAME _____ | **DATE** _____

Polygon Concepts Review

1 Circle the figure that is congruent to the figure above. When figures are congruent, they are exactly the same size *and* shape.

 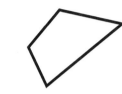 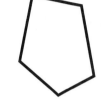 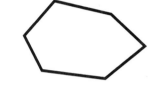

2 Circle the figure that has at least one right angle.

3 Circle the figure on which a line of symmetry has been drawn.

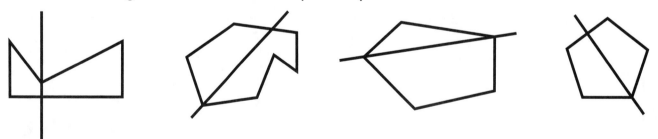

Explain how you can tell that the line on the figure you circled is a line of symmetry.

_____

_____

_____

_____

4

NAME

DATE

Frog Jump Multiplication, Record Sheet 2

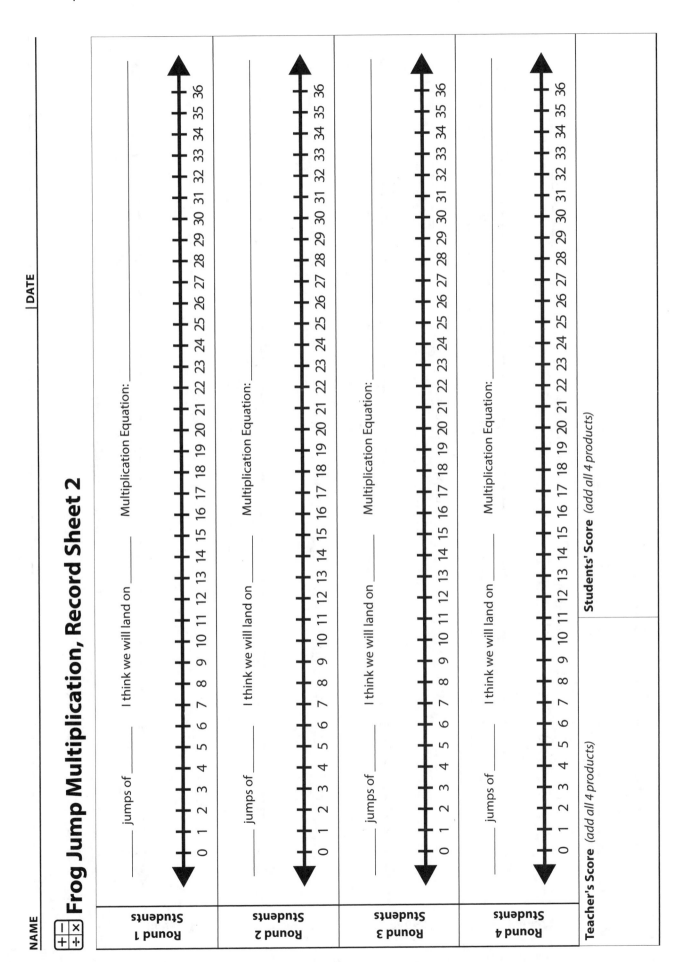

Round 1 Students

jumps of _____ I think we will land on _____ Multiplication Equation: _____

0 1 2 3 4 5 6 7 8 9 10 11 12 13 14 15 16 17 18 19 20 21 22 23 24 25 26 27 28 29 30 31 32 33 34 35 36

Round 2 Students

jumps of _____ I think we will land on _____ Multiplication Equation: _____

0 1 2 3 4 5 6 7 8 9 10 11 12 13 14 15 16 17 18 19 20 21 22 23 24 25 26 27 28 29 30 31 32 33 34 35 36

Round 3 Students

jumps of _____ I think we will land on _____ Multiplication Equation: _____

0 1 2 3 4 5 6 7 8 9 10 11 12 13 14 15 16 17 18 19 20 21 22 23 24 25 26 27 28 29 30 31 32 33 34 35 36

Round 4 Students

jumps of _____ I think we will land on _____ Multiplication Equation: _____

0 1 2 3 4 5 6 7 8 9 10 11 12 13 14 15 16 17 18 19 20 21 22 23 24 25 26 27 28 29 30 31 32 33 34 35 36

Teacher's Score *(add all 4 products)*

Students' Score *(add all 4 products)*

Frog Jump Multiplication, Record Sheet 3

Player 1 _____ Player 2 _____

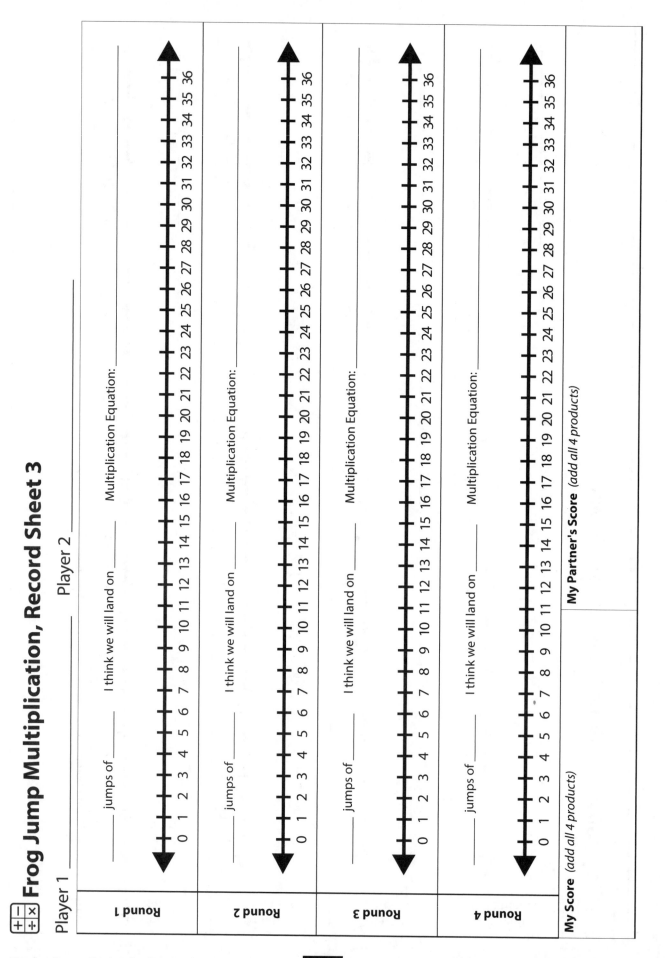

Round 1

_____ jumps of _____   I think we will land on _____   Multiplication Equation: _____

0 1 2 3 4 5 6 7 8 9 10 11 12 13 14 15 16 17 18 19 20 21 22 23 24 25 26 27 28 29 30 31 32 33 34 35 36

Round 2

_____ jumps of _____   I think we will land on _____   Multiplication Equation: _____

0 1 2 3 4 5 6 7 8 9 10 11 12 13 14 15 16 17 18 19 20 21 22 23 24 25 26 27 28 29 30 31 32 33 34 35 36

Round 3

_____ jumps of _____   I think we will land on _____   Multiplication Equation: _____

0 1 2 3 4 5 6 7 8 9 10 11 12 13 14 15 16 17 18 19 20 21 22 23 24 25 26 27 28 29 30 31 32 33 34 35 36

Round 4

_____ jumps of _____   I think we will land on _____   Multiplication Equation: _____

0 1 2 3 4 5 6 7 8 9 10 11 12 13 14 15 16 17 18 19 20 21 22 23 24 25 26 27 28 29 30 31 32 33 34 35 36

My Score *(add all 4 products)*

My Partner's Score *(add all 4 products)*

NAME | **DATE**

Changing Endpoints

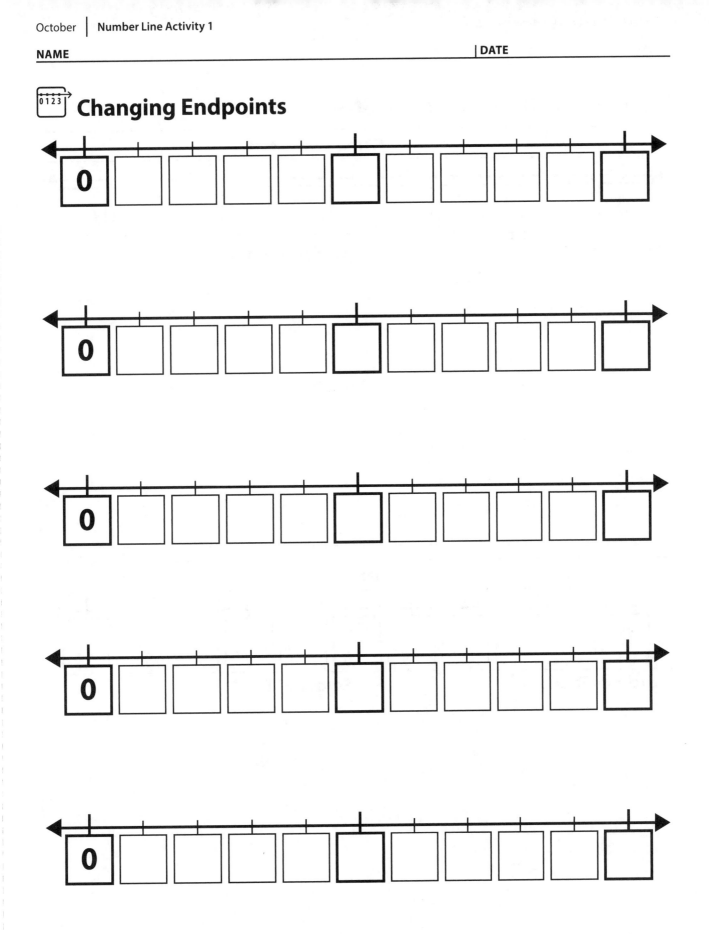

9

NAME | **DATE**

 Put It on the Line Record Sheet

Game 1	
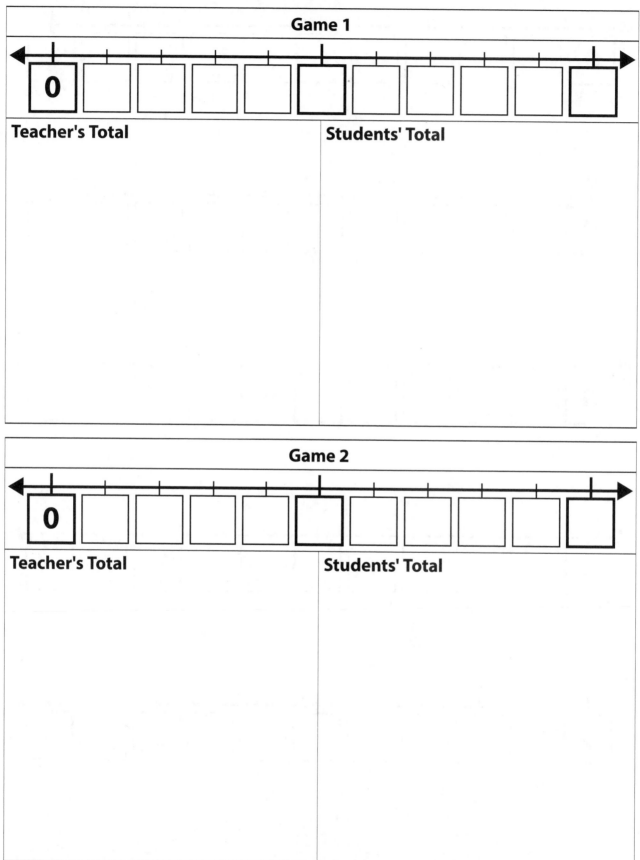	
Teacher's Total	**Students' Total**

Game 2	
0	
Teacher's Total	**Students' Total**

10

NAME _____ | **DATE** _____

🗓️ Rectangular Arrays

1 Label the dimensions of each array. Then find the total area of each rectangle. Try to find the area without counting every square. Finally, write a multiplication equation using the dimensions and area of the array.

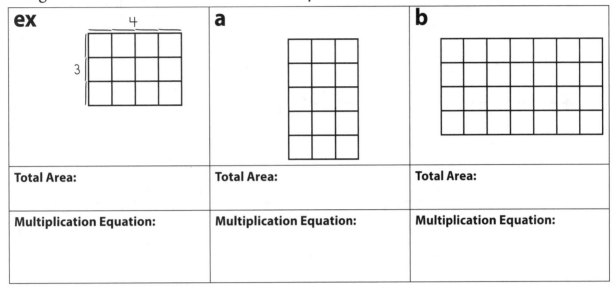

ex	**a**	**b**
Total Area:	Total Area:	Total Area:
Multiplication Equation:	Multiplication Equation:	Multiplication Equation:

2 Color in a 7-by-6 array on the grid. Label each dimension.

3 Then find the total area of the array. See if you can find a way to do it without counting each square one by one. Show your work below. You can use pictures, numbers, or words to show how you found the area.

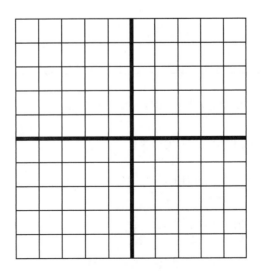

11

NAME _____ | **DATE** _____

🖐 Fractions on a Number Line

1 Label the missing numbers on these number lines. You can use improper fractions or mixed numbers (or both) to label the numbers greater than 1.

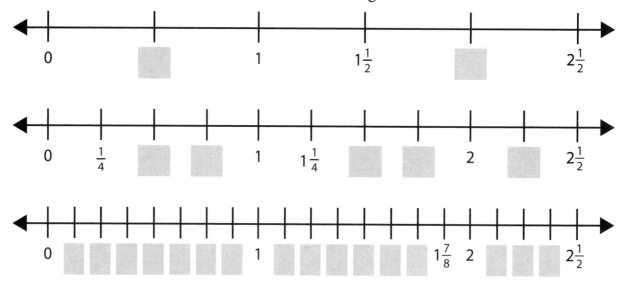

2 Use the number lines to help complete this table.

Improper Fraction	Mixed Number	How many $\frac{1}{2}$s?	How many $\frac{1}{4}$s?	How many $\frac{1}{8}$s?
$\frac{10}{4}$	$2\frac{2}{4}$	5	10	$\frac{20}{8}$
$\frac{12}{8}$				
$\frac{4}{2}$				

3 Use the number lines above to help answer the following questions.

a How many fourths are equal to $1\frac{1}{2}$?

b How many eighths are equal to $\frac{3}{4}$?

c How many fourths are equal to $2\frac{2}{8}$?

4 Write as many fractions and mixed numbers as you can think of that are equal to $2\frac{1}{2}$.

12

NAME _____ | DATE _____

 **Array Race** page 1 of 2

Player 1 _____   Player 2 _____

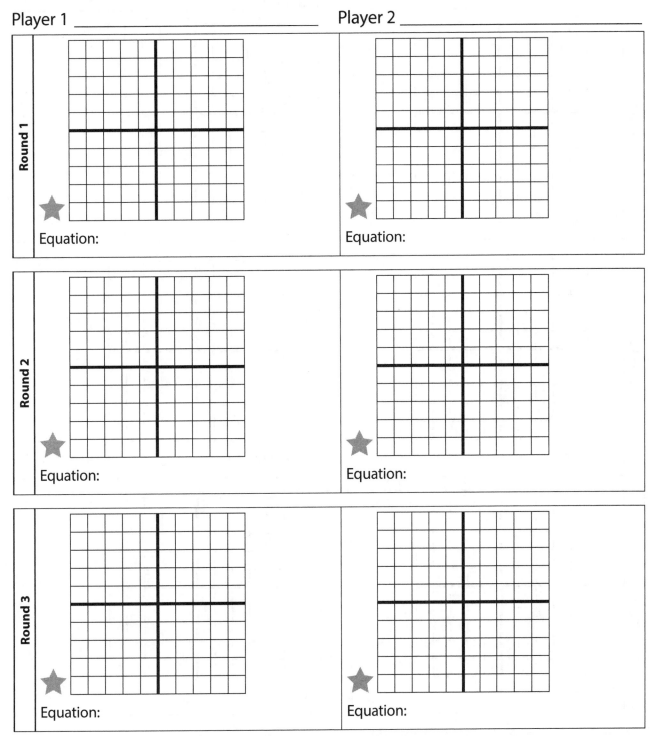

Score: Add the products from each round to find your score.

Player 1's Score	Player 2's Score

NAME _____ |**DATE** _____

Array Race page 2 of 2

Player 1 _____   Player 2 _____

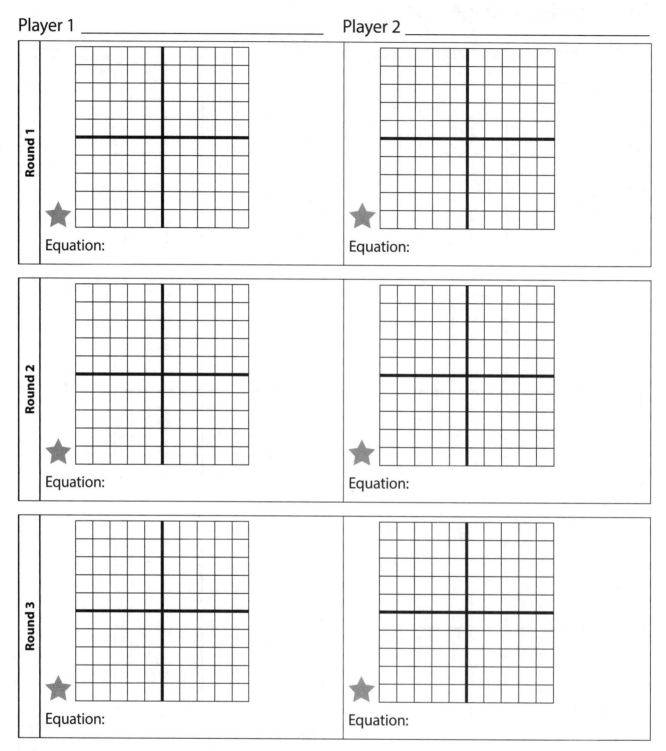

Score: Add the products from each round to find your score.

Player 1's Score	Player 2's Score

Round & Add

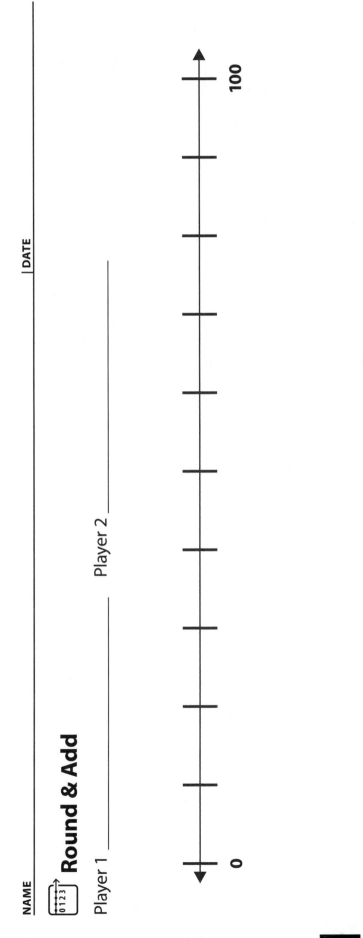

Player 1 _____

Player 2 _____

0

100

Player 1		Player 2	
Estimated Score:		**Estimated Score:**	
Exact Score:		**Exact Score:**	

NAME _____ | DATE _____

💡 Field Trips page 1 of 2

Tanika's third grade class is going on a field trip to the science museum. Help Tanika answer the following questions. For each question, be sure to show your work using pictures, numbers, or words.

1 Tickets to the museum cost $7 each. There are 8 students in Tanika's group. How much does it cost for Tanika's group to go to the science museum?

    a What is this problem asking you to figure out? Underline any information that can help you solve the problem.

    b Write an equation that represents the problem. Write your equation with a letter that stands for the unknown quantity.

    c Solve the problem. Show your work.

NAME _____ | DATE _____

Field Trips page 2 of 2

2 Tanika's group is studying animals. They visit two exhibits with turtles. There are 51 turtles in all. There are 25 turtles in one exhibit. How many turtles are in the other exhibit?

  a What is this problem asking you to figure out? Underline any information that can help you solve the problem.

  b Write an equation that represents the problem. Write your equation with a letter that stands for the unknown quantity.

  c Solve the problem. Show your work.

3 There are 27 students in Tanika's class. At lunch, they sit at 3 tables. If the same number of students sits at each table, how many students are at each table?

  a What is this problem asking you to figure out? Underline any information that can help you solve the problem.

  b Write an equation that represents the problem. Write your equation with a letter that stands for the unknown quantity.

  c Solve the problem. Show your work.

Thinking About Fractions

1 Write an equivalent fraction for each fraction below. Draw a labeled sketch that shows how the fractions are equivalent.

a $\frac{1}{3} = $ _____

b $\frac{2}{8} = $ _____

2 Why does $\frac{1}{4} + \frac{1}{4} + \frac{1}{4} = \frac{3}{4}$?

3 If December had 33 days, what would the 33rd calendar marker look like?

a Draw and label a sketch to show the 33rd calendar marker.

b Write two equations for the 33rd marker.

c Write one equivalent fraction for the 33rd marker.

_____ = _____

NAME _____ | **DATE** _____

⊞ Multiplying by Two

"Two Step" by Greg Tang

Two is very fast and fun;
quickly double and you're done.
What's that you say, be more precise?
Okay, then, just add it twice!

What is 2 × 8? It's 8 doubled.

2 × 8 = 8 + 8 = 16

1 Show your own example of the Doubles strategy.

2 Multiply each number in the grid by 2. Write each answer in the box. The first one is done for you.

5	7	3	1	11	8	12	6	2
10								
10	8	11	0	9	5	0	12	4

3 Use the Doubles strategy to help solve these combinations.

2 × 24 = _____   2 × 32 = _____   2 × 44 = _____   2 × 54 = _____

```
    29              33              125             230
  × 2             × 2             × 2             × 2
  ____            ____            _____           _____
```

Zero facts (× 0) ☐
Ones facts (× 1) ☐
Doubles facts (× 2) ☐
Doubles Plus One Set facts (× 3) ☐
Double-Doubles facts (× 4) ☐
Half-Tens facts (× 5) ☐
Half-Tens Plus One Set facts (× 6) ☐
Double-Double-Doubles facts (× 8) ☐
Tens Minus One Set facts (× 9) ☐
Tens facts (× 10) ☐

Multiplication Table

×	0	1	2	3	4	5	6	7	8	9	10
0	0	0	0	0	0	0	0	0	0	0	0
1	0	1	2	3	4	5	6	7	8	9	10
2	0	2	4	6	8	10	12	14	16	18	20
3	0	3	6	9	12	15	18	21	24	27	30
4	0	4	8	12	16	20	24	28	32	36	40
5	0	5	10	15	20	25	30	35	40	45	50
6	0	6	12	18	24	30	36	42	48	54	60
7	0	7	14	21	28	35	42	49	56	63	70
8	0	8	16	24	32	40	48	56	64	72	80
9	0	9	18	27	36	45	54	63	72	81	90
10	0	10	20	30	40	50	60	70	80	90	100

NAME _____ | DATE _____

⊞ Scout Them Out (0, 1, 2)

Multiplication

1 Circle all the Zero facts (× 0) in blue. Then go back and solve them.

2 Circle all the Ones facts (× 1) in red. Then go back and solve them.

3 Circle all the Doubles facts (× 2) in green. Then go back and solve them.

$$
\begin{array}{cccccc}
2 & 2 & 2 & 1 & 7 & 5 \\
\times 0 & \times 3 & \times 5 & \times 0 & \times 2 & \times 1
\end{array}
$$

$$
\begin{array}{cccccc}
8 & 5 & 8 & 0 & 3 & 2 \\
\times 0 & \times 1 & \times 2 & \times 4 & \times 1 & \times 2
\end{array}
$$

$$
\begin{array}{cccccc}
9 & 9 & 9 & 3 & 1 & 2 \\
\times 0 & \times 1 & \times 2 & \times 0 & \times 1 & \times 6
\end{array}
$$

$$
\begin{array}{cccccc}
7 & 1 & 2 & 6 & 2 & 10 \\
\times 0 & \times 4 & \times 4 & \times 0 & \times 1 & \times 0
\end{array}
$$

Division

4 Solve the following division problems if you like. Can you use what you know about multiplication to help?

$1\overline{)2}$ $2\overline{)10}$ $1 \div 1 = \underline{\hspace{2cm}}$ $1\overline{)7}$ $8 \div 2 = \underline{\hspace{2cm}}$

$1\overline{)8}$ $2\overline{)2}$ $3 \div 1 = \underline{\hspace{2cm}}$ $1\overline{)13}$ $10 \div 2 = \underline{\hspace{2cm}}$

$1\overline{)9}$ $\overline{)8}^{\,4}$ $6 \div 1 = \underline{\hspace{2cm}}$ $\overline{)5}^{\,5}$ $12 \div 2 = \underline{\hspace{2cm}}$

$\overline{)7}^{\,7}$ $2\overline{)16}$ $4 \div 1 = \underline{\hspace{2cm}}$ $1\overline{)12}$ $14 \div 2 = \underline{\hspace{2cm}}$

21

NAME _____ | **DATE** _____

📦 More Rounding Practice

1 Round the numbers below to the nearest ten. When you round to the nearest ten, look at the number in the ones place. If it is 5 or higher, round up to the next highest ten. If it is less than 5, keep the number in the tens place the same.

ex 63 60	**ex** 186 190	47	52
35	94	122	856
267	993	1,247	2,052

2 Round the numbers below to the nearest hundred. When you round to the nearest hundred, look at the number in the tens place. If it is 5 or higher, round up to the next highest hundred. If it is less than 5, keep the number in the hundreds place the same.

ex 163 200	**ex** 627 600	**ex** 82 100	203
254	822	439	67
153	764	449	657

3 Write two different numbers that round up or down to each number shown.

ex 400 438 384	20	80
100	300	700

NAME _____ | **DATE** _____

Round & Add Hundreds

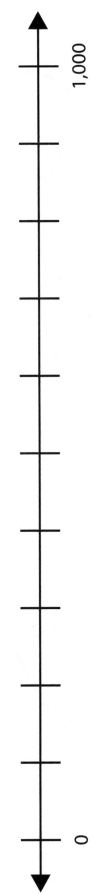

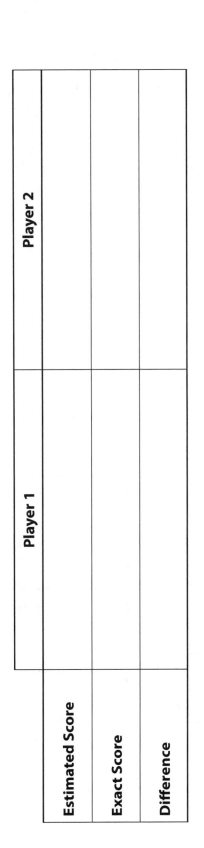

	Player 1	Player 2
Estimated Score		
Exact Score		
Difference		

Fraction Concepts Review

1   Label each fraction.

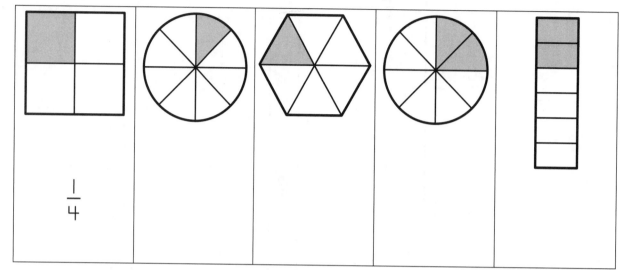

$\frac{1}{4}$

2   Shade in the shapes to show the fraction above. Show two different ways to create each fraction.

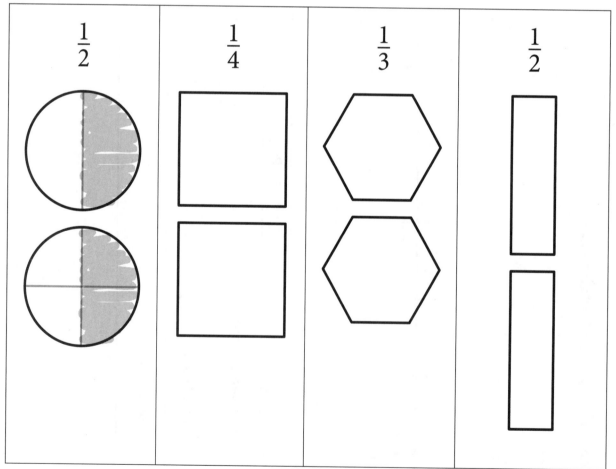

$\frac{1}{2}$ $\frac{1}{4}$ $\frac{1}{3}$ $\frac{1}{2}$

NAME _____ | **DATE** _____

 Time

1 What time is it?

2 Choose one of the clocks above and figure out what time it was 15 minutes ago and what time it will be 15 minutes from now. Circle the clock you chose.

a 15 minutes ago: _____

b 15 minutes from now: _____

3 Paula went to the library at 3:15. She left the library at 3:50 and went outside to the park. She stayed at the park for 20 minutes and then left to go home. It took her 15 minutes to walk home.

a How long did Paula stay at the library? Explain your thinking.

b What time did Paula get home? Explain your thinking.

4 Max's bus leaves at 8:05. It takes him 5 minutes to get dressed, 15 minutes to eat breakfast, and 10 minutes to walk to the bus. If Max gets up at 7:30, will he get to his bus on time?

NAME _____ |**DATE** _____

⊞ Multiplying by Ten

"Perfect Ten" by Greg Tang

Ten is such a breeze to do,

all because of place value.

To quickly multiply by 10,

put a zero at the end.

What is 10 × 9? It's 9 with a zero on the end.

$$10 \times 9 = 90$$

1 Show your own example of the "add a zero to the end of the number" strategy.

2 Multiply each number in the grid by 10. Write each answer in the box. The first one is done for you.

5	7	3	1	11	8	12	6	2
50								
10	8	11	0	9	5	0	12	4

3 Use the strategy of adding a zero to the end of the number, or your own strategy, to help solve these combinations:

10 × 15 = _____   10 × 25 = _____   10 × 31 = _____   10 × 59 = _____

$$\begin{array}{r} 14 \\ \times\ 10 \\ \hline \end{array} \qquad \begin{array}{r} 20 \\ \times\ 10 \\ \hline \end{array} \qquad \begin{array}{r} 35 \\ \times\ 10 \\ \hline \end{array} \qquad \begin{array}{r} 40 \\ \times\ 10 \\ \hline \end{array}$$

Multiplying by Five

"Five Alive" by Greg Tang

Five will yield the right amount

if by 5s you always count.

Or else just multiply by 10;

half will get you there again!

What is 5×8? It's ten 8s divided in half.

$$5 \times 8 = (10 \times 8) \div 2$$
$$= 80 \div 2$$
$$= 40$$

1 Show your own example of multiplying by 10 and dividing in half to multiply by 5.

2 Multiply each number in the grid by 5. Write each answer in the box. The first one is done for you.

5	7	3	1	11	8	12	6	2
25								
10	8	11	0	9	5	0	12	4

3 Use the strategy of multiplying by 10 and dividing in half, or your own strategy, to help solve these combinations:

$5 \times 15 =$ _____ $5 \times 20 =$ _____ $5 \times 25 =$ _____ $5 \times 50 =$ _____

$$\begin{array}{r} 16 \\ \times\ 5 \\ \hline \end{array}$$
$$\begin{array}{r} 100 \\ \times\ 5 \\ \hline \end{array}$$
$$\begin{array}{r} 30 \\ \times\ 5 \\ \hline \end{array}$$
$$\begin{array}{r} 200 \\ \times\ 5 \\ \hline \end{array}$$

NAME _____ | **DATE** _____

⊞ Scout Them Out (10, 5)

Multiplication

1 Circle all the Tens facts (× 10) in red. Then go back and solve them.

2 Circle all the Half-Tens facts (× 5) in blue. Then go back and solve them.

9	7	10	9	5	6
× 10	× 5	× 4	× 5	× 5	× 5

8	5	10	10	4	6
× 5	× 3	× 10	× 8	× 5	× 10

3	5	4	5	8	7
× 10	× 7	× 10	× 10	× 10	× 10

1	1	2	3	2	3
× 10	× 5	× 10	× 5	× 5	× 10

Division

3 Solve the following division problems if you like. Can you use what you know about multiplication to help?

$10\overline{)80}$ $10\overline{)40}$ $70 \div 10 =$ _____ $5\overline{)45}$ $30 \div 5 =$ _____

$5\overline{)40}$ $5\overline{)50}$ $30 \div 10 =$ _____ $10\overline{)70}$ $25 \div 5 =$ _____

$10\overline{)90}$ $\overline{)100}^{\,10}$ $60 \div 10 =$ _____ $5\overline{)5}$ $10 \div 5 =$ _____

$10\overline{)20}$ $10\overline{)30}$ $15 \div 5 =$ _____ $10\overline{)10}$ $50 \div 10 =$ _____

28

NAME _____ | **DATE** _____

💡 Making Cookies

Solve each problem. Show your thinking with numbers, pictures, or words. Be sure to show your final answer clearly.

1 Alexis is making cookies. She made 58 chocolate cookies and 37 ginger cookies. Then, she gave 76 cookies to her school's bake sale. How many cookies did Alexis have left?

2 Max has 2 cookie trays. He can put 4 rows of 6 cookies on one cookie tray and 7 rows of 8 cookies on another cookie tray. How many cookies can he put on his 2 cookie trays?

💡 Food Drive: Estimating & Reasoning

Make an estimate for each problem. Then, solve the problem. Show your thinking. Finally, think about your answer. Is it reasonable? Is it similar to your estimate?

1 Petra's school is having a canned food drive. Petra's third grade class brings in 289 cans of food. The other third grade class brings in 315 cans. How many more cans does the third grade need to collect 750 cans of food?

 a What's your estimate? Why?

 b Solve the problem:

 c Is your answer reasonable? Why or why not?

2 Marcos is in charge of counting cans for the food drive. He organizes the cans in 6-by-8 arrays, and he has 10 of these arrays. Does he have at least 500 cans?

 a What's your estimate? Why?

 b Solve the problem:

 c Is your answer reasonable? Why or why not?

Solving Area & Perimeter Problems

When you answer the questions below, remember that perimeter is the distance around the outside of a figure and area is the total number of square units it takes to cover the figure.

1a The beetle is going to take a walk around the perimeter of this rectangle. How many linear units will she have to travel to get all the way around?

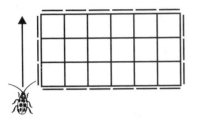

   b   What is the area of this rectangle?

2a What is the perimeter of this rectangle?

   b   What is the area of this rectangle?

3a What is the perimeter of this rectangle?

   b   What is the area of this rectangle?

4a Enter information about the rectangle in questions 1, 2, and 3 on this chart.

Rectangle	Perimeter	Area
1		
2		
3		

   b   What do you notice about the perimeters and areas?

NAME _____ | DATE _____

Fractions of a Dollar page 1 of 2

1 Complete the table.

Coin		Fraction of a Dollar	Cents
1 dime		$\dfrac{1}{10}$	10¢
1 quarter			
1 half dollar			
3 dimes			
5 dimes			
8 dimes			
2 quarters			
3 quarters			
3 half dollars			
6 half dollars			

(continued on next page)

Fractions of a Dollar page 2 of 2

2 Show each fraction on a dollar grid. Then circle the fraction that is greater in each row.

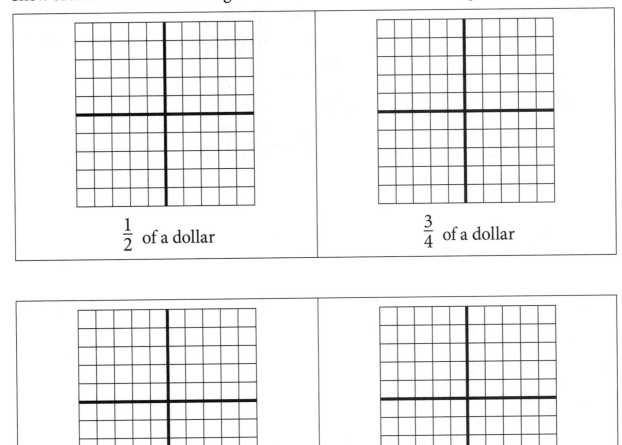

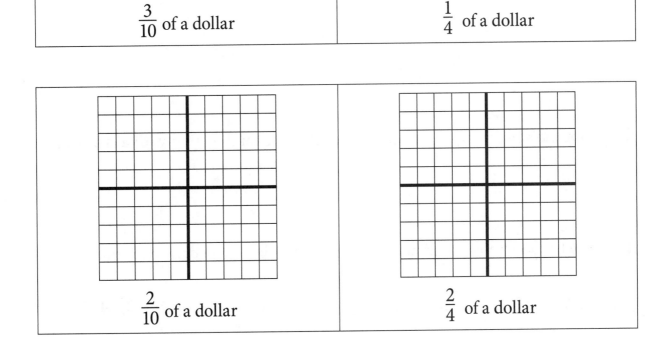

⊞ Multiplying by Three

"Three Sum" by Greg Tang

Three is as easy as can be,

if you triple what you see.

In other words just add it thrice,

this simply is once more than twice!

What is 3×9?
It's 9 doubled plus 9.

$3 \times 9 = (9 + 9) + 9$

$27 = 18 + 9$

$18 + 9 = 27$

1 Show your own example of the Doubles Plus One Set strategy.

$$3 + 4 = 7$$

2 For each box below, multiply the number in the corner by 3. Write each answer in the box. The first one is done for you.

^{5} 15	^{7} 21	^{3} 9	^{1} 3	^{11} 33	^{8} 24	^{12} 36	^{6} 18	^{2} 6

3 Use the Doubles Plus One Set strategy to help solve these combinations:

$3 \times 13 = \underline{39}$ $3 \times 25 = \underline{100}$ $3 \times 33 = \underline{99}$ $3 \times 40 = \underline{120}$

$$\begin{array}{r} 30 \\ \times\ 3 \\ \hline 90 \end{array} \qquad \begin{array}{r} 100 \\ \times\ 3 \\ \hline 300 \end{array} \qquad \begin{array}{r} 125 \\ \times\ 3 \\ \hline 200 \end{array} \qquad \begin{array}{r} 210 \\ \times\ 3 \\ \hline 430 \end{array}$$

4 Write and solve your own Doubles Plus One Set combination with a larger number.

$$8 + 9 = 17$$

5 Use what you know about multiplying by 3 to solve these division problems.

$12 \div 3 = \underline{4}$ $21 \div 3 = \underline{7}$ $3\overline{)18}$ with 6 above $3\overline{)24}$ with 8 above

NAME _____ | **DATE** _____

⊞ Multiplying by Four

"Four Eyes" by Greg Tang

Four is very fast to do
when you multiply by 2.
Here's a little good advice —
please just always double twice.

What is 4×7?
It's 7 doubled twice.

Double once: $7 + 7 = 14$

Double twice: $14 + 14 = 28$

---

1 Show your own example of the Double-Doubles strategy.

2 Multiply each number in the grid by 4. Write each answer in the box. The first one is done for you.

20 ⁵	28 ⁷	12 ³	4 ¹	44 ¹¹	32 ⁸	48 ¹²	24 ⁶	8 ²

3 Use the Double-Doubles strategy to help solve these combinations:

$4 \times 15 = \underline{60}$ $4 \times 25 = \underline{100}$ $4 \times 35 = \underline{140}$ $4 \times 50 = \underline{200}$

$$\begin{array}{r} 14 \\ \times\ 4 \\ \hline 56 \end{array} \qquad \begin{array}{r} 100 \\ \times\ 4 \\ \hline 400 \end{array} \qquad \begin{array}{r} 30 \\ \times\ 4 \\ \hline 120 \end{array} \qquad \begin{array}{r} 200 \\ \times\ 4 \\ \hline 800 \end{array}$$

4 Write and solve your own Double-Doubles combination with a larger number.

$1000 \times 4 = 4000$

5 Use what you know about multiplying by 4 to solve these division problems.

$12 \div 4 = \underline{3}$ $16 \div 4 = \underline{4}$ $4\overline{)24} \ ^{6}$ $4\overline{)40} \ ^{10}$

⊞ Multiplying by Eight

"Crazy Eight" by Greg Tang

Eight is very much like 4;

simply double but once more.

Since 2 times 2 times 2 is 8,

doubling 3 times works just great!

What is 8 × 7?

It's 7 doubled 3 times.

Double once: 7 + 7 = 14

Double twice: 14 + 14 = 28

Double three times: 28 + 28 = 56

1 Show your own example of the Double-Double-Doubles (double 3 times) strategy.

$$8 \times 8 = 64$$

2 Do you have another good strategy for multiplying by 8? If so, show an example.

NOPE

3 Multiply each number in the grid by 8. Write each answer in the box. The first one is done for you.

5	7	3	1	11	8	12	6	2
40	56	24	8	88	64	96	48	16

4 Use the Double-Double-Doubles strategy to help solve these combinations:

8 × 15 = 120   8 × 25 = 200   8 × 35 = 280   8 × 50 = 400

$$\begin{array}{r} 14 \\ \times\ 8 \\ \hline 102 \end{array}$$
$$\begin{array}{r} 100 \\ \times\ 8 \\ \hline 800 \end{array}$$
$$\begin{array}{r} 30 \\ \times\ 8 \\ \hline 240 \end{array}$$
$$\begin{array}{r} 150 \\ \times\ 8 \\ \hline 1200 \end{array}$$

5 Write and solve your own Double-Double-Doubles combination with a larger number.

$$8 \times 200 = 1,600$$

6 Use what you know about multiplying by 8 to solve these division problems.

16 ÷ 8 = 2   24 ÷ 8 = 3 $8\overline{)32}$ = 4 $8\overline{)40}$ = 5

NAME _____ | DATE _____

Scout Them Out (3, 4, 8)

Multiply by Three, Four and Eight Practice

1 Circle all the Doubles Plus One Set facts (×3) in red. Then go back and solve them.

2 Circle all the Double-Doubles facts (×4) in blue. Then go back and solve them.

3 Circle all the Double-Double-Doubles facts (×8) in green. Then go back and solve them.

9	7	10	9	5	6
× 4	× 3	× 4	× 8	× 3	× 8
48	21	40	72	15	48
8	5	10	10	4	6
× 8	× 4	× 3	× 8	× 3	× 4
64	20	30	80	12	24
3	5	4	2	3	7
× 3	× 8	× 4	× 8	× 4	× 3
9	40	16	16	12	21
1	1	2	3	2	3
× 4	× 8	× 4	× 8	× 4	× 4
4	8	8	24	8	12
1	6	9	3	8	7
× 3	× 3	× 4	× 5	× 4	× 4
3	18	36	15	32	28

Divide by Three, Four and Eight Practice

4 Solve the division problems. Can you use what you know about multiplication to help?

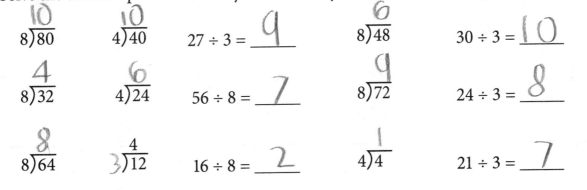

8)80 = 10   4)40 = 10   27 ÷ 3 = 9   8)48 = 6   30 ÷ 3 = 10

8)32 = 4   4)24 = 6   56 ÷ 8 = 7   8)72 = 9   24 ÷ 3 = 8

8)64 = 8   3)12 = 4   16 ÷ 8 = 2   4)4 = 1   21 ÷ 3 = 7

NAME _____ | **DATE** _____

⌨ **Fraction Number Lines**

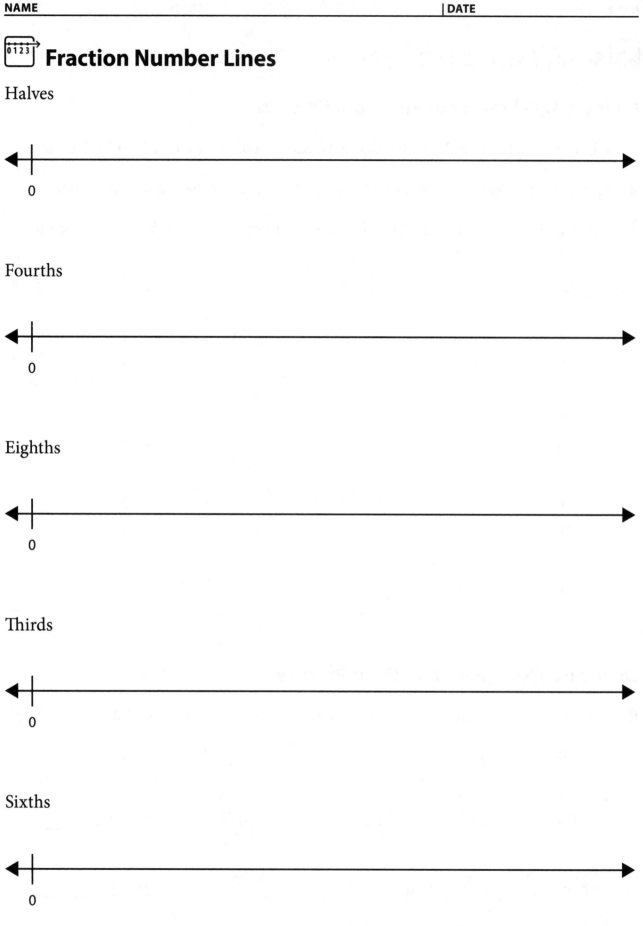

Halves

0

Fourths

0

Eighths

0

Thirds

0

Sixths

0

NAME _____ | **DATE** _____

 # Extended Fraction Number Lines

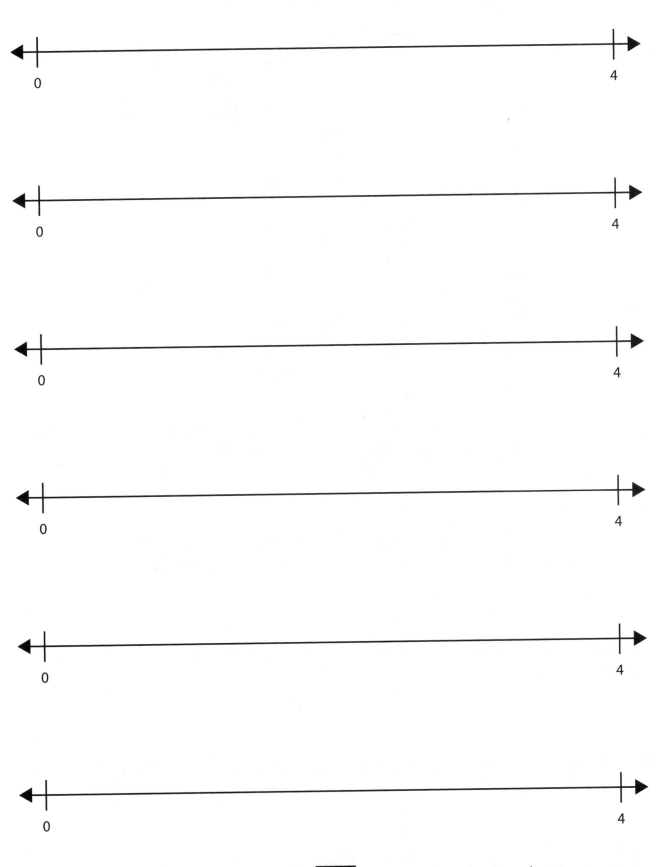

NAME _____ |DATE _____

💡 Kilograms of Food Served

Use the bar graph to answer the questions below.

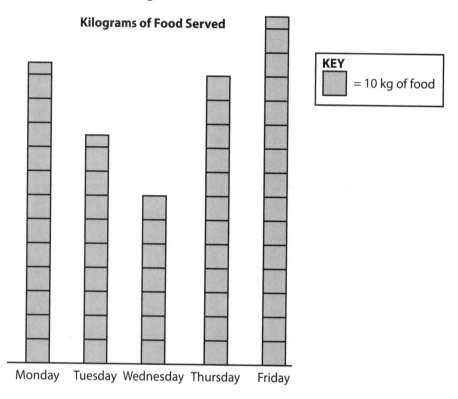

Kilograms of Food Served

KEY
⬜ = 10 kg of food

Monday Tuesday Wednesday Thursday Friday

1 On which day was the most food served? (When was the maximum amount of food served?) What was the amount of food served that day?

2 On which day was the least amount of food served? (When was the minimum amount of food served?) What was the amount of food served that day?

3 What is the difference between the minimum and maximum amounts? (What is the range?)

4 Was there more food served on Monday and Tuesday or on Wednesday and Friday? How do you know?

40

NAME _______________________________ | DATE _______________

Make Your Own Bar Graph

Use the data from your class survey to fill in the graph below. Remember to fill in the title and key and to include labels for the bars.

Key

Title _______________________________

NAME _____ |DATE

Data Story Problems

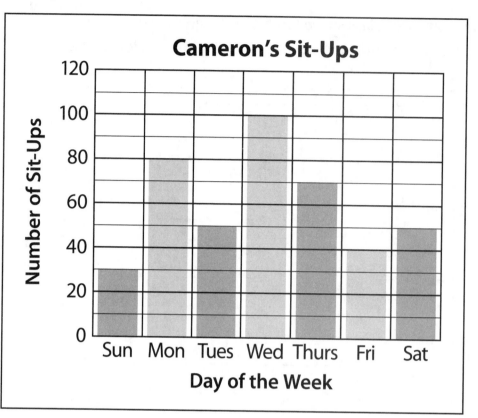

1 On what day did Cameron do the most sit-ups? How many sit-ups did he do that day?

2 One what day did Cameron do the fewest sit-ups? How many did he do that day?

3 What is the difference between the number of sit-ups he did on the two days above?

4 Did Cameron do more sit-ups on Monday and Friday combined, or on Sunday, Tuesday, and Saturday combined?

NAME _____ | **DATE** _____

Grid page 1 of 2

43

NAME _____ | **DATE** _____

Grid page 2 of 2

⊞ Multiplying by Nine

"Nine Ball" by Greg Tang

Nine is faster to compute

if at first you overshoot.

Here's a very clever tack,

do 10 times and then subtract!

What is 9×7?
It's ten 7s minus 7.

$$9 \times 7 = (10 \times 7) - 7$$
$$= 70 - 7$$
$$= 63$$

1 Show your own example of the Tens Minus One Set strategy.

2 Do you have another good strategy for multiplying by 9? If so, show an example.

3 Multiply each number in the grid by 9. Write each answer in the box. The first one is done for you.

5	7	3	1	11	8	12	6	2
45								
10	8	11	0	9	5	0	12	4

4 Use the Tens Minus One Set strategy, or your own strategy, to solve these combinations.

$9 \times 15 =$ _____ $9 \times 25 =$ _____ $9 \times 30 =$ _____ $9 \times 50 =$ _____

$$\begin{array}{r} 14 \\ \times\ 9 \\ \hline \end{array}$$
$$\begin{array}{r} 100 \\ \times\ 9 \\ \hline \end{array}$$
$$\begin{array}{r} 30 \\ \times\ 9 \\ \hline \end{array}$$
$$\begin{array}{r} 40 \\ \times\ 9 \\ \hline \end{array}$$

5 Write and solve your own Tens Minus One Set combination with a larger number.

6 Use what you know about multiplying by 9 to solve these division problems.

$18 \div 9 =$ _____ $27 \div 9 =$ _____ $9\overline{)45}$ $9\overline{)54}$

⊞ Multiplying by Six

"Six Sense" by Greg Tang

When multiplying by six
Don't worry. You're not in a fix.
Multiply by 10 and take half.
Then add in one more
And you're out the door.

What is 6×4? Think Half-Tens and One More Set.

$4 \times 10 = 40$. Half 40 is 20. Add one more 4 and you're out the door. $20 + 4 = 24$!

1 Show your own example of the Half-Tens Plus One Set strategy.

2 Do you have another good strategy for multiplying by 6? If so, show an example.

3 Multiply each number in the grid by 6. Write each answer in the box. The first one is done for you.

5	7	3	1	11	8	12	6	2
30								
10	8	11	0	9	5	0	12	4

4 Use the Half-Tens Plus One Set strategy, or your own strategy, to solve these combinations.

$6 \times 15 = $ _____ $6 \times 20 = $ _____ $6 \times 33 = $ _____ $6 \times 50 = $ _____

$$\begin{array}{r} 25 \\ \times\ 6 \\ \hline \end{array} \qquad \begin{array}{r} 100 \\ \times\ 6 \\ \hline \end{array} \qquad \begin{array}{r} 30 \\ \times\ 6 \\ \hline \end{array} \qquad \begin{array}{r} 150 \\ \times\ 6 \\ \hline \end{array}$$

5 Write and solve your own Half-Tens Plus One Set combination with a larger number.

6 Use what you know about multiplying by 9 to solve these division problems.

$12 \div 6 = $ _____ $24 \div 6 = $ _____ $6\overline{)30}$ $6\overline{)18}$

Scout Them Out (6, 9)

Multiply by 9 & 6 Practice

1 Circle all the Tens Minus One Set facts (×9) in red. Then go back and do them.

2 Circle all the Half-Tens Plus One Set (×6) in blue. Then go back and do them.

9	6	9	6	5	6
× 10	× 5	× 4	× 8	× 9	× 3

8	4	10	0	4	6
× 9	× 6	× 6	× 9	× 9	× 10

8	6	4	5	9	7
× 6	× 7	× 9	× 9	× 9	× 9

1	10	2	3	2	3
× 6	× 9	× 9	× 6	× 9	× 9

9	6	9	6	2	9
× 6	× 6	× 8	× 0	× 6	× 3

Divide by 9 & 6 Practice

3 Solve the following division problems if you like. Can you use what you know about multiplication to help?

$10\overline{)90}$ $10\overline{)60}$ $72 \div 9 =$ _____ $5\overline{)45}$ $30 \div 5 =$ _____

$6\overline{)48}$ $9\overline{)54}$ $30 \div 6 =$ _____ $9\overline{)81}$ $24 \div 6 =$ _____

$3\overline{)27}$ $\overline{)90}^{\,10}$ $60 \div 10 =$ _____ $6\overline{)6}$ $12 \div 2 =$ _____

$6\overline{)18}$ $6\overline{)36}$ $36 \div 9 =$ _____ $1\overline{)9}$ $63 \div 9 =$ _____

Find the Fraction Number Line 1

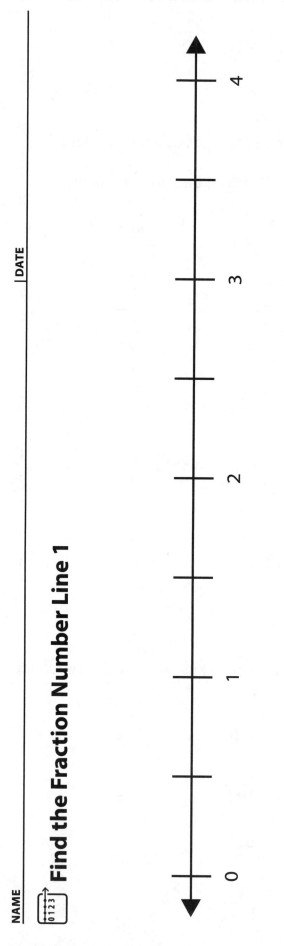

0   1   2   3   4

NAME

DATE

Find the Fraction Number Line 2

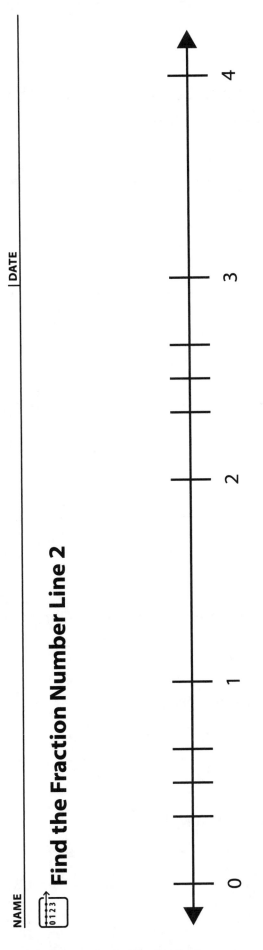

NAME _____ **DATE** _____

Comparing Fractions

1 Draw a colored bar from 0 to the point on the number line that shows the location for the fractions listed to the left of each number line.

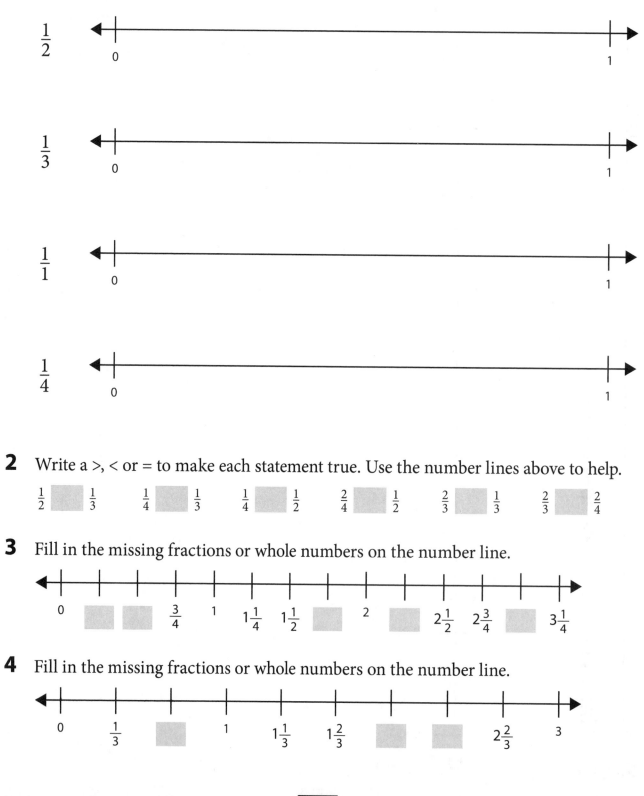

2 Write a >, < or = to make each statement true. Use the number lines above to help.

$\frac{1}{2}$ ▢ $\frac{1}{3}$ $\frac{1}{4}$ ▢ $\frac{1}{3}$ $\frac{1}{4}$ ▢ $\frac{1}{2}$ $\frac{2}{4}$ ▢ $\frac{1}{2}$ $\frac{2}{3}$ ▢ $\frac{1}{3}$ $\frac{2}{3}$ ▢ $\frac{2}{4}$

3 Fill in the missing fractions or whole numbers on the number line.

4 Fill in the missing fractions or whole numbers on the number line.

💡 Perimeter Puzzles

1 Max walked around the edge of his yard. How far did he walk? What is the area of Max's yard? Don't forget to use the correct units.

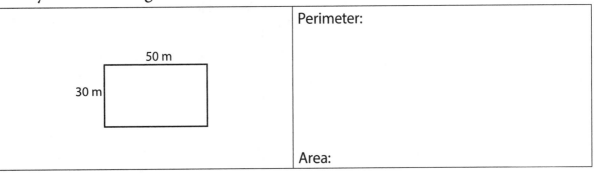

Perimeter:

Area:

2 What is the perimeter of the shape below?

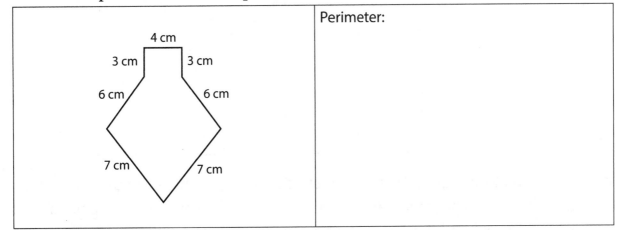

Perimeter:

3 Claudia has an L-shaped tree fort. She knows the perimeter of the tree fort is 24 feet. She knows the lengths of 5 of the 6 sides. What is the length of the other side?

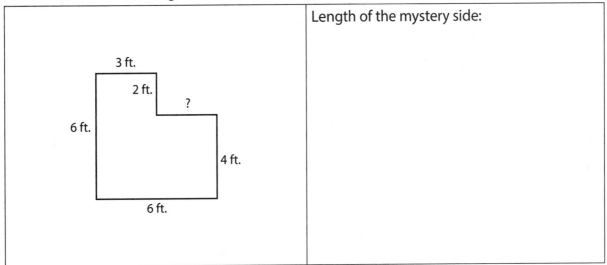

Length of the mystery side:

Same Perimeter, Different Area

1 Make two rectangles that have a perimeter of 20 units, but different areas.

Rectangle 1:	Rectangle 2:
Area:	Area:

2 Sergio is making a quilt. He has 16 meters of edging. What size quilts can Sergio make that have a perimeter of 16 meters? Draw and label two rectangular shapes that Sergio could use for his quilt. Show the area of each quilt.

NAME _____ | DATE _____

💡 Freddy's Community Center

1 Freddy swims at the community center each week. He wonders about the area of the pool. He thinks he cannot figure it out because the pool is not rectangular. Can you figure out the area of the swimming pool at Freddy's community center?

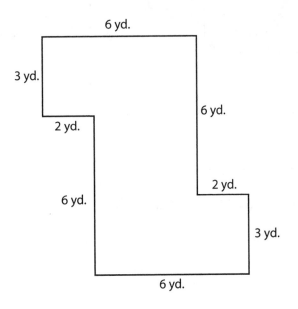

2 Freddy's community center is building a new sandbox. They know they want the sandbox to be a rectangle with an area of 18 square feet but they are not sure what the perimeter should be. Draw two different rectangles with an area of 18 square feet. Show the perimeter of each one.

More About Fractions

1 Label each calendar marker below with at least one fraction name.

Calendar Marker	6	7	8	9	10
1st Fraction Name					
2nd Fraction Name					

2 List at least two ways in which the calendar markers above are alike.

3 LaTonya says that all of these markers show $\frac{1}{3}$ of something. Do you agree with her? Why or why not?

4 Which is more, $\frac{2}{6}$ or $\frac{1}{2}$? How do you know?

5 Color in $\frac{1}{3}$ of the eggs in this carton.

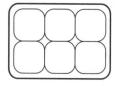

NAME _____ | DATE _____

🎨 Time Fractions Story Problems

Show your work to solve the following:

1 At 2:05 Tom said that school is over in three-quarters of an hour. What time is school over?

2 At 1:30 Deb's friend called and said, "Let's meet at the mall in one and one-third hours." What time are they meeting?

3 Bob said the movie starts in half an hour. If it is 2:15, what time does the movie start?

4 At 6:45 Jamie's dad said she had to go to bed in one and three-quarters of an hour. What time does Jamie have to go to bed?

5 At 2:15 Cal's mom said that he could play video games for one and a half hours. What time does Cal have to stop playing video games?

6 At 7:50 Don said his favorite show starts in two-thirds of an hour. What time does the show start?

7 Gym class is over in two-fourths of an hour. If it is 1:30 now, what time will gym class be over?

8 The recital lasted for one and a quarter hours. It ended at 3:30. What time did it start?

55

⊞ Quick Facts Worksheet A

What's your multiplier?	How many minutes?	Number correct

1 Multiply each number in the grid by your multiplier. Write each product in the box.

5	7	3	6	1	0	2	10
4	6	11	9	12	8	4	5
6	10	2	7	8	1	9	3
9	7	12	2	11	0	8	10
11	12	3	4	7	6	5	9

2 Choose *10 different* products from above (except 0) and record them in the 10 boxes below. Then divide each by your multiplier.

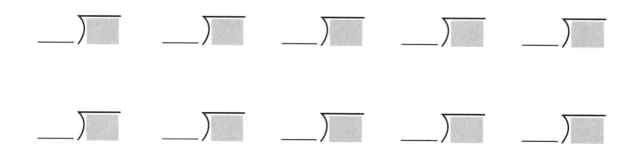

⊞ **Quick Facts Worksheet B**

What's your multiplier?	How many minutes?	Number correct

1 Multiply each number in the grid by your multiplier. Write each product in the box.

5	7	3	6	1	0	2	10
4	6	11	9	12	8	4	5
6	10	2	7	8	1	9	3
9	7	12	2	11	0	8	10
11	12	3	4	7	6	5	9

2 Choose *10 different* products from above (except 0) and record them in the 10 boxes below. Then divide each by your multiplier.

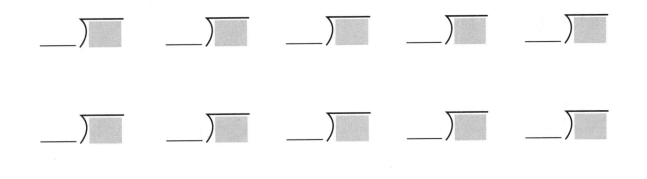

⊞ Quick Facts Worksheet C

What's your multiplier?	How many minutes?	Number correct

1 Multiply each number in the grid by your multiplier. Write each product in the box.

5	7	3	6	1	0	2	10
4	6	11	9	12	8	4	5
6	10	2	7	8	1	9	3
9	7	12	2	11	0	8	10
11	12	3	4	7	6	5	9

2 Choose *10 different* products from above (except 0) and record them in the 10 boxes below. Then divide each by your multiplier.

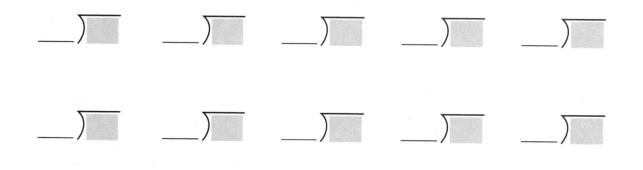

NAME _____ | **DATE** _____

⊞ Quick Facts Tracking Sheet

When you get back your Quick Facts Worksheet from last time:

- Record the date you completed the sheet, the time it took you, and the number of facts you got correct.
- If it took you more than 2 minutes or you got fewer than 38 facts correct, write "no" in the last box in the row and use that same multiplier or set of multipliers again.
- If you completed 38 or more facts correctly in 2 minutes or less, write "yes" the last box in the row and choose another multiplier or set of multipliers.
- Cross out each number as you master the facts for that multiplier or range of multipliers. Then circle your next target.

| 2 | 3 | 4 | 5 | 6 | 7 | 8 | 9 | 10 | 2–6 | 4–9 | 0–10 |

Multiplier or Range of Multipliers	Date	Time Taken	Correct Facts	Mastered? (at least 38 correct in 2 min. or less)

NAME _____ | **DATE** _____

Rows & Columns Multiplication Game

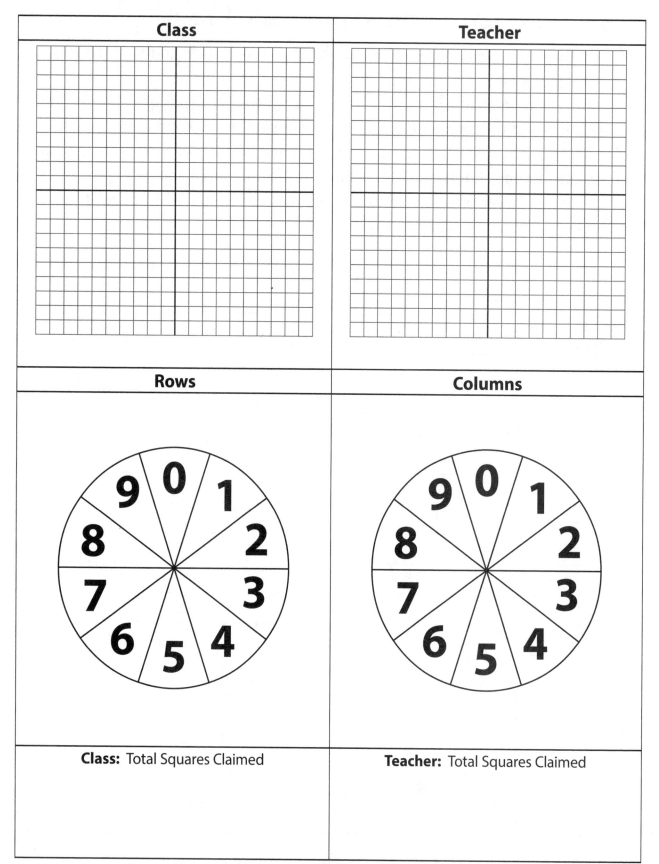

Class	Teacher
Rows	Columns

Class: Total Squares Claimed

Teacher: Total Squares Claimed

NAME _____ | **DATE** _____

Multiplication & Division Problems 3 page 1 of 2

1 For each array, show how you can break it into smaller arrays to find the product. Then write a multiplication and division fact family for the array.

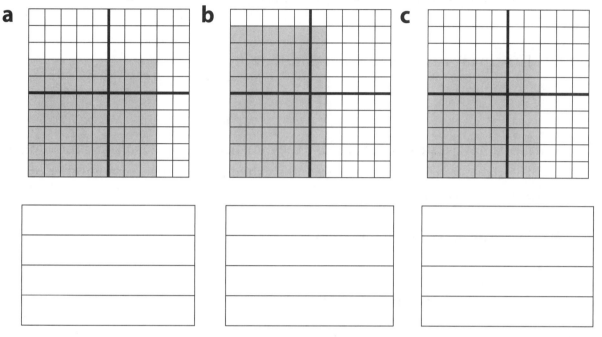

a   **b**   **c**

2 Complete each equation by filling in the missing number.

 = 3 × 7   7 × = 21   21 ÷ = 7

7 = 56 ÷   8 × = 56   8 = 56 ÷

3 Look over your last Quick Facts page and select three combinations that were challenging for you. Draw an array for each one, and show how you can divide the array into smaller arrays to find the product.

NAME _____ | **DATE** _____

Multiplication & Division Problems 3 page 2 of 2

4 Marianna is getting barrettes to share with her sisters. She bought 4 packages, and each package has 8 barrettes.

   a Write an equation to represent this problem.

   b How many barrettes did Marianna buy in all?

5 Marianna has 3 sisters. On Saturday they washed cars to earn some money. All 4 of the sisters worked on her own and washed exactly the same number of cars. Altogether, they washed 24 cars.

   a Write an equation to represent this problem.

   b How many cars did each sister wash?

6 **CHALLENGE** Write your own multiplication problem and include an equation.

7 **CHALLENGE** Write your own division problem and include an equation.

💡 Multiplication & Division Problems 4 page 1 of 2

1 For each array, show how you can break it into smaller arrays to find the product. Then write a multiplication and division fact family for the array.

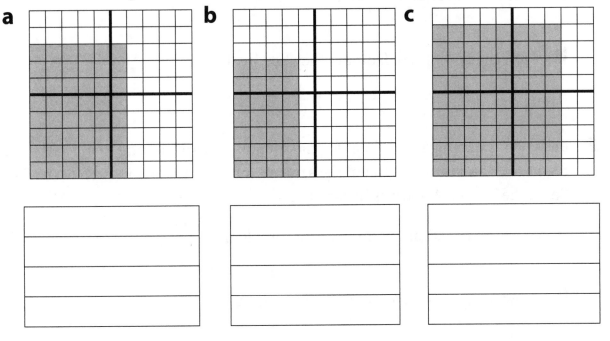

a   **b**   **c**

2 Complete each equation by filling in the missing number.

$8 \times 4 =$ ☐ $64 =$ ☐ $\times 8$ $48 = 8 \times$ ☐ $24 \div 8 =$ ☐

$6 \times 3 =$ ☐ $36 =$ ☐ $\times 6$ $42 = 6 \times$ ☐ $54 \div 6 =$ ☐

3 Look over your last Quick Facts page and select three combinations that were challenging for you. Draw an array for each one, and show how you can divide the array into smaller arrays to find the product.

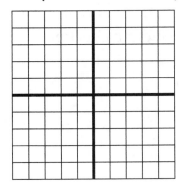   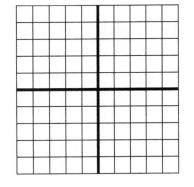

NAME _____ |DATE _____

Multiplication & Division Problems 4 page 2 of 2

4 Rashawn and his dad are getting ready for a party. They bought 2 bags that each had 7 oranges in them and 5 bags that each had 7 apples in them.

   a Write an equation to represent this problem.

   b How many pieces of fruit did they buy in all?

5 Rashawn is making goody bags for the friends who are coming to his party. He has 63 marbles and he wants to put the same number of marbles in each of the 9 bags. So far, he has put 4 marbles in each bag.

   a Write an equation to represent this problem.

   b How many more marbles will he put in each bag?

6 <u>CHALLENGE</u> Write your own multiplication story problem and include an equation.

7 <u>CHALLENGE</u> Write your own division story problem and include an equation.

NAME _____ |**DATE** _____

Area & Fractions

1 Shade in part of this rectangle to match the green region on marker 2.

2 Write at least two fractions to show what fraction of the whole rectangle is represented by the shaded region.

3 Shade in a fraction of the rectangle that is greater than the fraction from marker 2. Write an inequality statement showing which fraction is greater.

4 Shade in a fraction of the rectangle that is less than the fraction from marker 2. Write an inequality statement showing which fraction is greater.

NAME | **DATE**

Fractions of Other Areas

1   Look at the rectangles and fill in the table below.

   a   Find the area of each rectangle outlined below and write it in the table.

   b   Shade in $\frac{1}{6}$ of each rectangle. Label each shaded region with its area.

   c   What would be the area of a region that represented $\frac{5}{6}$ of each rectangle? Write your answers in the table.

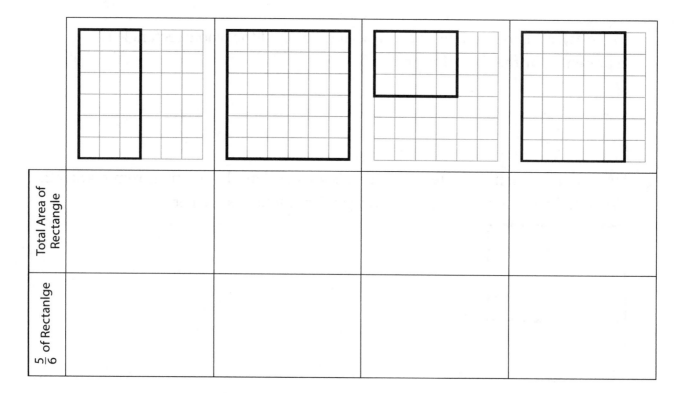

Total Area of Rectangle			
$\frac{5}{6}$ of Rectanlge			

2   Imagine you were given a rectangle with an area of 120.

   a   If you shaded in $\frac{1}{6}$ of the rectangle, what would be the area of the shaded region?

   b   If you shaded in $\frac{5}{6}$ of the rectangle, what would be the area of the shaded region?

Areas of Rectilinear Figures

1 Show 3 different ways to find the area of the outlined figure. Label all your work.

2 a Look carefully at the figure below and make a quick estimate of its area.

b Show 3 different ways to find the area of the outlined figure. Label all your work. Then circle the way you think is most efficient, elegant, or interesting.

3 CHALLENGE Show 3 different ways to find the area of the outlined figure. Label all your work. Then circle the way you think is most efficient, elegant, or interesting.

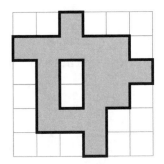
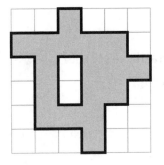
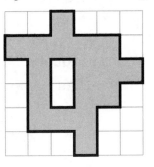

Area & Fractions Story Problems page 1 of 2

Solve each problem. Show all your work. Respond to each part of every problem.

1 Ramone and his family were planning their garden using this grid. Each square on the grid represents 1 square yard. This shows one way they could make their garden.

Family Garden, Plan A

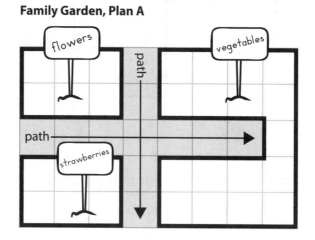

a How big is the family's garden in square yards (including the paths)?

b How many square yards are used for vegetables? What fraction of the garden is used for vegetables?

c How many square yards are used for flowers? What fraction of the garden is used for flowers?

d How many square yards are used for strawberries? What fraction of the garden is used for strawberries?

2 Write an equation or inequality statement showing whether each fraction above is greater than, less than, or equal to $\frac{1}{2}$.

(continued on next page)

Area & Fractions Story Problems page 2 of 2

3 Ramone and his family were not all pleased with Plan A. Help them make Plan B, based on different family members' requests.

- Ramone's mom said she wanted more than half of the garden to be used for vegetables.

- Ramone said he wanted there to be at least 4 square yards for flowers so that they could cut flowers for their grandparents sometimes.

- Ramone's little sister said she wanted the strawberry section to be larger than the flower section.

a What is the smallest area they would need for the vegetables?

b Draw a plan B that could work for Ramone, his sister, and his mom.

c Draw a different plan B that could also work for the family.

NAME _____ | DATE _____

Roll & Multiply Data Chart

Date	Total Odd Products	Total Even Products	Total Products

1 Label the axes on the graph to the right so you can show the data from the chart on it.

2 Draw a bar graph to represent the data from the chart.

3 Based on the data, how would you describe the chance of getting an odd number when you roll and multiply?

○ impossible

○ unlikely

○ equally likely or unlikely

○ likely

○ certain

4 How would you describe the chance of getting an even number when you roll and multiply?

○ impossible

○ unlikely

○ equally likely or unlikely

○ likely

○ certain

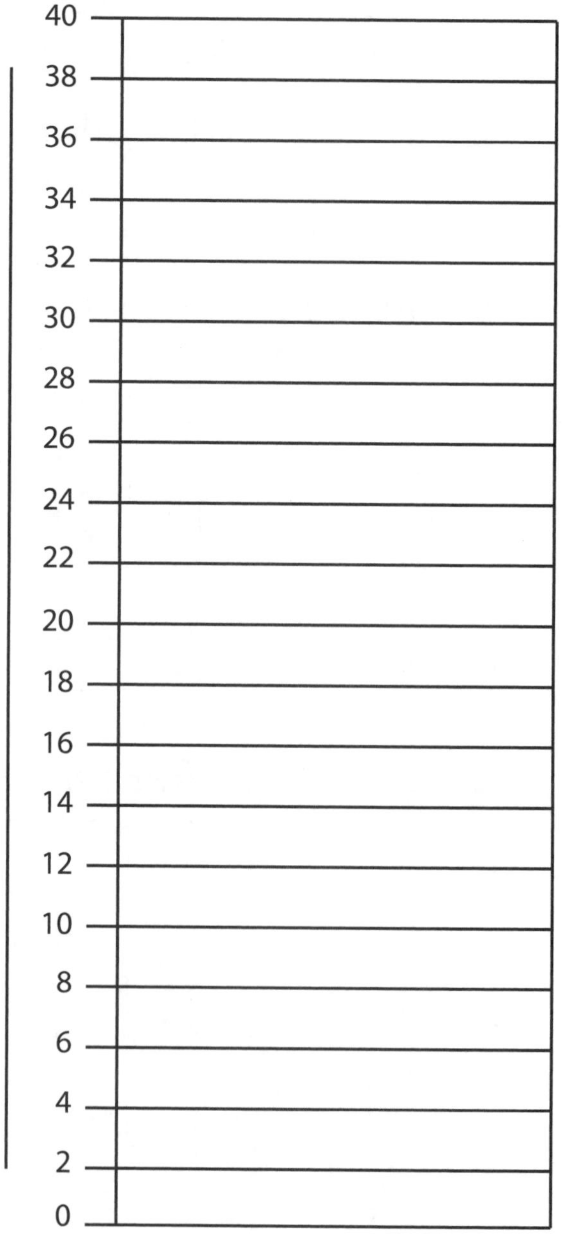

40
38
36
34
32
30
28
26
24
22
20
18
16
14
12
10
8
6
4
2
0

NAME _____ | DATE _____

 Thinking About Roll & Multiply

Date	Total Odd Products	Total Even Products	Total Products

1 What observations can you make about the data above?

2 Fill in the missing numbers on this multiplication table. Then color in the squares with odd products.

×	4	5	6	7	8	9
4	16	20	24		32	
5	20		30	35		45
6	24		36		48	
7	28	35		49	56	63
8	32		48		64	
9		45	54	63		81

3 a How many products are there in all on the multiplication table? _____

b How many of those products are odd? _____

c How many of those products are even? _____

d What does this tell you about the Roll & Multiply experiment?

NAME _____ **| DATE** _____

One More Look at Roll & Multiply

1 Fill in the chart below with the total number of odd and even products rolled so far.

Date	Total Odd Products	Total Even Products	Total Products

2 a Circle the pie graph below that you think comes closest to showing the results of your experiment so far.

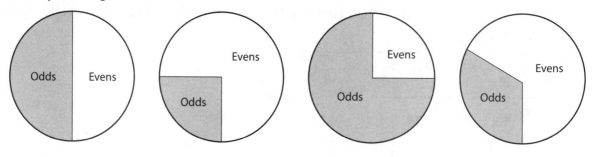

b Explain your choice above.

NAME _____ | DATE _____

⊞ Ten to Win Multiplication Game

Partner Record Sheet

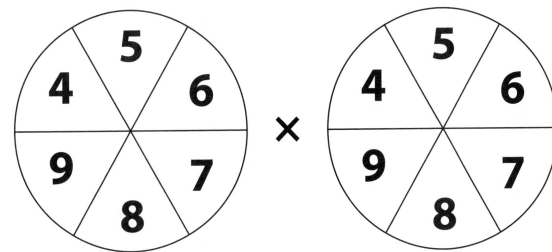

16	20	20	24	24	25	28	28	30
30	32	32	35	35	36	36	36	40
40	42	42	45	45	48	48	49	54
54	56	56	63	63	64	72	72	81

Partner 1

_____

_____

_____

_____

_____

Partner 2

_____

_____

_____

_____

_____

Multiplication & Division Problems 1 page 1 of 2

1 Solve each multiplication problem. Then use it to solve the related problems below.

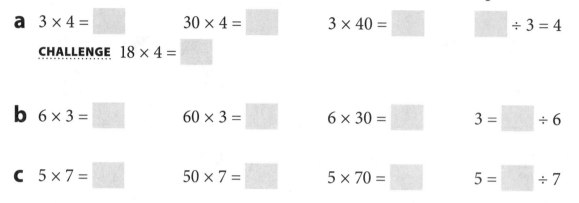

a $3 \times 4 =$ ▢ $30 \times 4 =$ ▢ $3 \times 40 =$ ▢   ▢ $\div 3 = 4$

    CHALLENGE $18 \times 4 =$ ▢

b $6 \times 3 =$ ▢ $60 \times 3 =$ ▢ $6 \times 30 =$ ▢ $3 =$ ▢ $\div 6$

c $5 \times 7 =$ ▢ $50 \times 7 =$ ▢ $5 \times 70 =$ ▢ $5 =$ ▢ $\div 7$

2 Complete each maze. Write equations below each one to show how you found the path from Start to End.

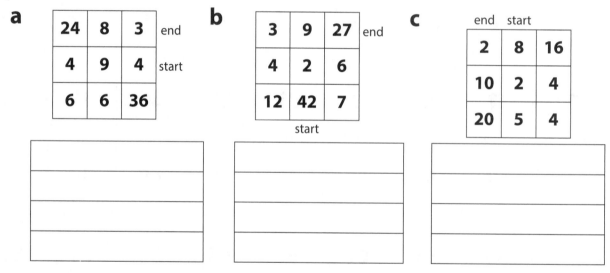

a

24	8	3	end
4	9	4	start
6	6	36	

b

3	9	27	end
4	2	6	
12	42	7	

start

c

end   start

2	8	16
10	2	4
20	5	4

3 Look over your last Quick Facts page and select three combinations that were challenging for you. Draw an array for each one and show how you can divide the array into smaller arrays to find the product.

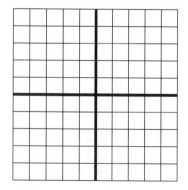
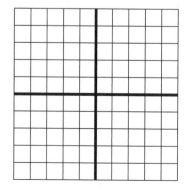
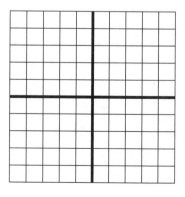

Multiplication & Division Problems 1 page 2 of 2

4 Monica was bagging cookies at her uncle's bakery. Her uncle asked her to put 8 cookies in each bag. There were 72 cookies in all. How many bags will she fill?

a Write an equation to represent this problem.

b How many bags will Monica fill?

5 Mrs. Jackson bought boxes of cards at the store. There were 9 cards in each box, and she bought 7 boxes. How many cards did she buy in all?

a Write an equation to represent this problem.

b How cards did Mrs. Jackson buy?

6 **CHALLENGE** Write your own multiplication story problem and include an equation.

7 **CHALLENGE** Write your own division story problem and include an equation.

Multiplication & Division Problems 2

1 Solve each multiplication problem. Then use it to solve the related problems.

a $7 \times 4 =$ ☐ $70 \times 4 =$ ☐ $7 \times 40 =$ ☐   ☐ $\div 7 = 4$

CHALLENGE $14 \times 4 =$ ☐

b $8 \times 6 =$ ☐ $80 \times 6 =$ ☐ $8 \times 60 =$ ☐   ☐ $\div 8 = 6$

CHALLENGE $16 \times 6 =$ ☐

c $5 \times 9 =$ ☐ $50 \times 9 =$ ☐ $5 \times 90 =$ ☐   ☐ $\div 5 = 9$

CHALLENGE $5 \times 18 =$ ☐

2 Complete each puzzle by filling in the missing numbers. The product of the two numbers goes on top. The sum of the two numbers goes on the bottom.

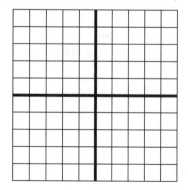
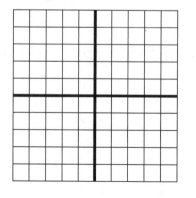
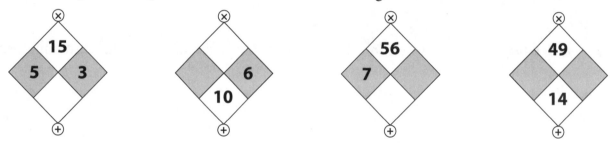
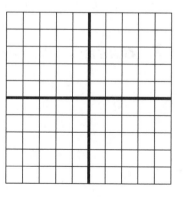

3 Look over your last Quick Facts page and select three combinations that were challenging for you. Draw an array for each one and show how you can divide the array into smaller arrays to find the product.

Multiplication & Division Problems 2 page 2 of 2

4   Jin and his brother Huang were comparing their collections of toy cars. Jin said, "I have 8 times as many cars as you have!" Huang has 5 cars.

   a   Write an equation to represent this problem.

   b   How many cars does Jin have?

5   Elisa has 8 stickers. She wanted more stickers, so her friends gave her more, and now she has 6 times as many stickers.

   a   Write an equation to represent this problem.

   b   How many stickers did Elisa have after her friends gave some to her?

6   **CHALLENGE** Solve these diamond puzzles.

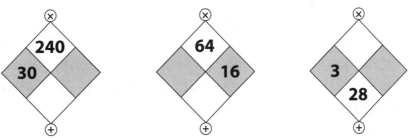

7   **CHALLENGE** Make your own diamond puzzles and trade with a classmate.

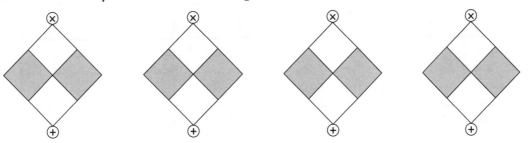

☀️ Multiplication & Division Problems 3

1 Solve each multiplication problem. Then use it to solve the related problems.

a $7 \times 9 =$ [　] $70 \times 9 =$ [　] $7 \times 90 =$ [　]   [　] $\div 7 = 9$

   CHALLENGE $14 \times 9 =$ [　]

b $9 \times 9 =$ [　] $90 \times 9 =$ [　] $9 \times 90 =$ [　]   [　] $\div 9 = 9$

   CHALLENGE $90 \times 90 =$ [　]

c $6 \times 7 =$ [　] $60 \times 7 =$ [　] $6 \times 70 =$ [　]   [　] $\div 7 = 6$

   CHALLENGE $6 \times 14 =$ [　]

2 Complete each puzzle by filling in the missing numbers. The product of the two numbers goes on top. The sum of the two numbers goes on the bottom.

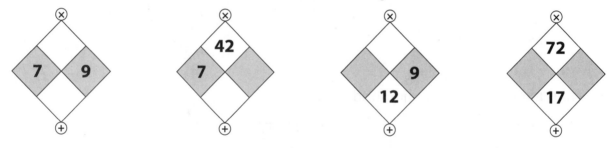

3 Look over your last Quick Facts page and select three combinations that were challenging for you. Draw an array for each one and show how you can divide the array into smaller arrays to find the product.

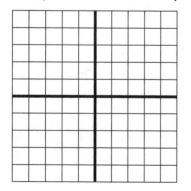

NAME _____ | DATE _____

Multiplication & Division Problems 3 page 2 of 2

4 The zookeeper was telling students about a kind of snake at the zoo. She said, "The snake is about 3 feet long when it hatches. By the time it is an adult, it can be 9 times as long!"

    a Write an equation to represent this problem.

    b How long can this snake be as an adult?

5 Mr. Jones is cutting ribbon for the students in his art class to use in a project. The piece of ribbon he has is 36 feet long and he wants to cut it into 9 equal pieces.

    a Write an equation to represent this problem.

    b How long is each of the 9 pieces?

6 **CHALLENGE** Solve these diamond puzzles.

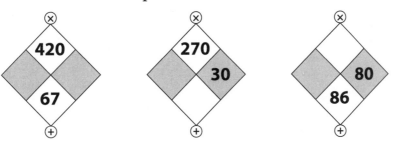

7 **CHALLENGE** Make your own diamond puzzles and trade with a classmate.

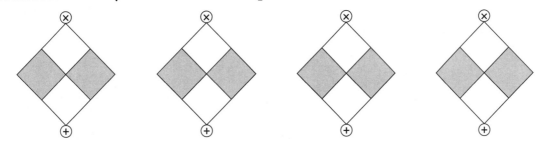

Problem String Work Space

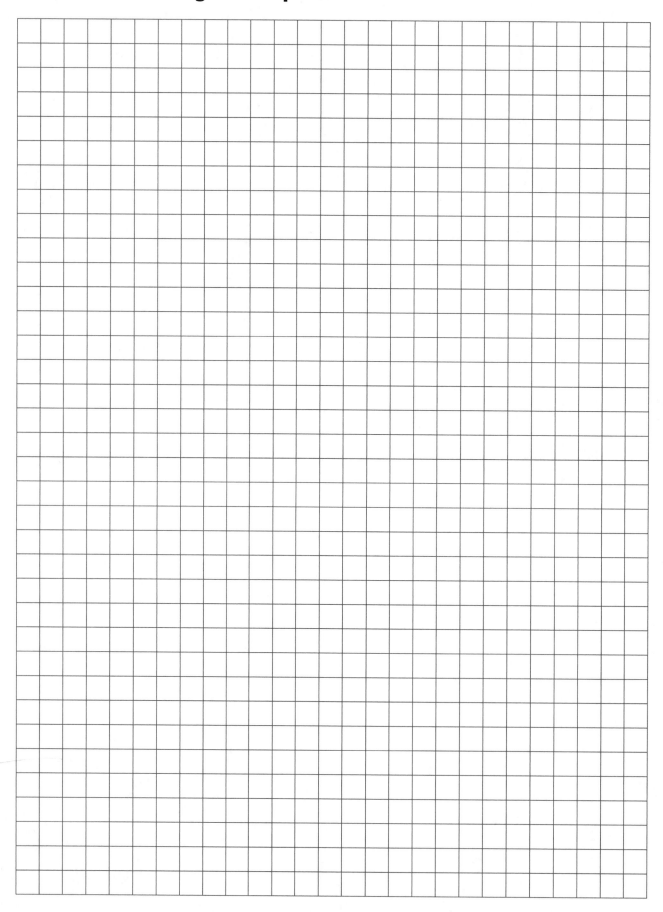

Problem String Work Space

Problem String Work Space

Problem String Work Space

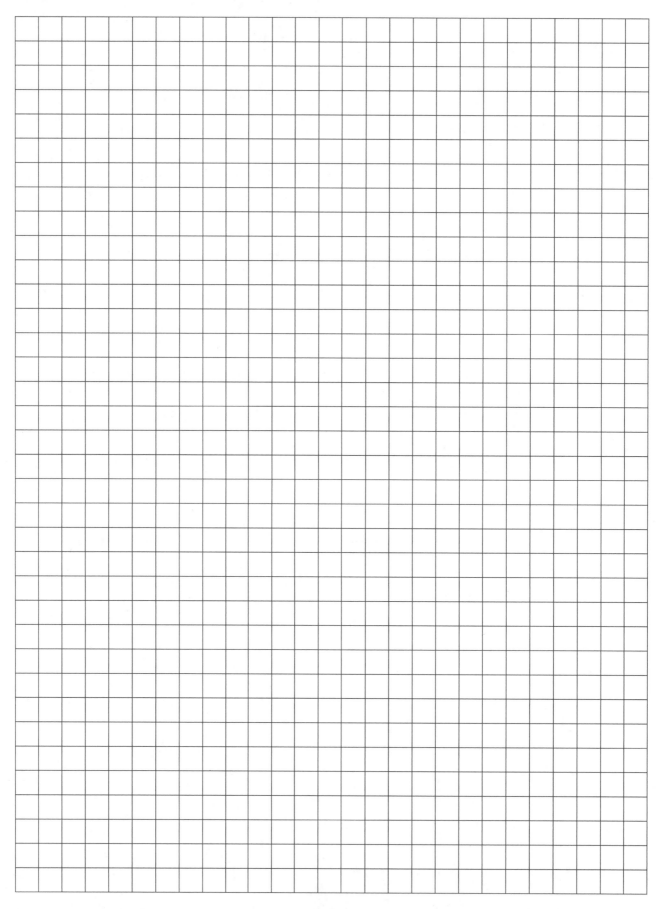

A4

🔳 Problem String Work Space

Problem String Work Space

Problem String Work Space

Problem String Work Space